THIS BOOK BELONGS TO:

Baby Shark: Annual 2021
A CENTUM BOOK 978-1-913399-82-5
Published in Great Britain by Centum Books Ltd
This edition published 2020
1 3 5 7 9 10 8 6 4 2

No part of this publication may be reproduced, stored in a retrieval system,
or transmitted in any form or by any means, electronic, mechanical, photocopying,
recording or otherwise, without the prior permission of the publishers.
Centum Books Ltd, 20 Devon Square, Newton Abbot, Devon, TQ12 2HR, UK
books@centumbooksltd.co.uk
CENTUM BOOKS Limited Reg. No. 07641486
A CIP catalogue record for this book is available from the British Library.
Printed in China.

pinkfong

BABY SHARK™

ANNUAL

Stories, colouring,
puzzles and doodling

2021
ANNUAL

Contents

8 Hello, Sharks!

10 Colours of the ocean

12 Birthday doodle

14 Sad or happy?

15 Dotty friends

16 Story: Daddy Shark

24 How many sea creatures?

25 Sunken ship

26 Hooray for beach day

27 Build with Baby Shark!

28 Find some treasure!

30 Shark Family Orchestra

32 Story: Daddy Shark

40 Spot the difference

42 Find and colour

44 Busy sea!

46 Balloons for everyone

48 Story: Daddy Shark

56 Shadow sharks

57 Join in!

58 Picture time!

60 Shark spiral

61 Sharky jokes

62 Find the family

64 Hide and seek

65 Hammerhead Shark's home!

66 Shark encounter!

67 Spot the difference

68 Family time

70 Find Baby Shark

71 Odd one out

72 Friends forever

73 Singing time

74 Where's Baby Shark?

76 Answers

See answers on pages 76–77.

Hello, Sharks!

Read about your favourite shark family!

Baby Shark

Baby Shark lives under the ocean and is curious about everything around him. He likes to sing. When he's scared, he sings to help him feel brave.

Mummy Shark

There are no limits to the things that Mummy Shark can do! She always listens to Baby Shark and they share a very special bond.

Daddy Shark

Daddy Shark is a strong and mighty hunter. He is much more than just Baby Shark's father though, the two of them play together like best friends!

Grandma Shark

Grandma Shark likes to read. She is a kind and thoughtful grandma who always has time to spend with Baby Shark.

Grandpa Shark

Grandpa Shark is wise and smart. He is famous for his hot clam buns and he loves to share his love of cooking with Baby Shark.

There are so many sea creatures for Baby Shark to play with!

Colours of the ocean

Under the sea is the place to be! Look at all the colourful sea creatures out and about today. Read the colour quiz questions, find the creatures in the picture and then circle your answers.

'We love colours, doo-doo-doo-doo-doo-doo!'

Colour quiz questions

1. What colour is Baby Shark?
2. What colour is Daddy Shark?
3. What colour is Mummy Shark?
4. What colour is Grandma Shark?
5. What colour is Grandpa Shark?
6. What colour is the jellyfish?
7. What colour is the starfish?
8. What colour is the turtle?

'All around, doo-doo-doo-doo-doo-doo!'

Birthday doodle

It's Baby Shark's birthday!
Draw him some presents.
What has he been given?

Sad or happy?

Baby Shark likes to pull funny faces, can you draw him some more?

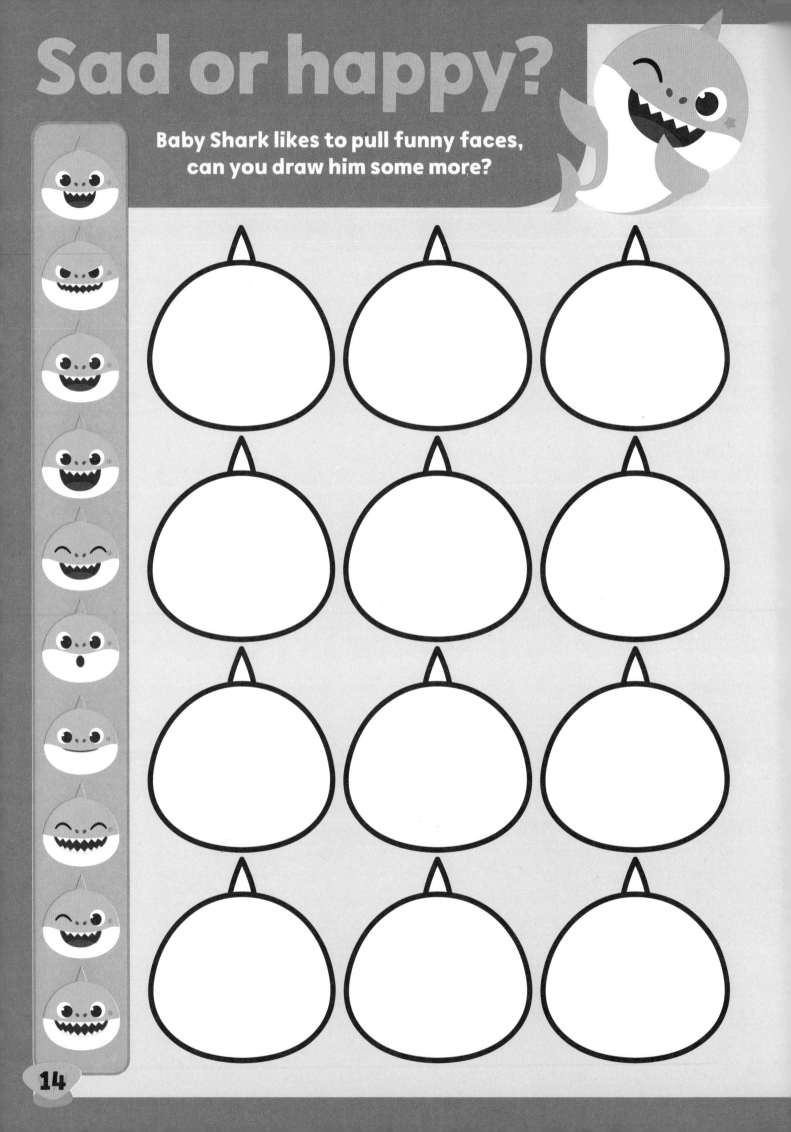

Dotty friends

Baby Shark is having a party. Who is coming to it? Join the dots to find out.

LOVE

15

Daddy Shark

Baby Shark loves going on adventures with Daddy Shark.

Today they are going
to hunt for treasure!

Mummy Shark waves
them off, she is going
to do some painting!

Baby Shark and Daddy Shark
swim away singing.

'Doo-doo-doo-doo-doo-doo!'

First they go to see Grandma Shark and Grandpa Shark. They have a map for them. It tells them where to go to look for the treasure!

START

FINISH!

Treasu

"This map says we have to follow the clues to find the treasure," says Daddy Shark. "Number one is, I'm blue and orange. Jump on board and I'll take you to clue number two. What could that mean, Baby Shark?"

Follow the clues to find the treasure.

Clue 1

I'm blue and orange. Jump on board and I' take you to clu number two

Baby Shark thinks very hard, then he sees
something coming round the bend,
"It's Fish Bus!" he shouts.

CONTINUED
ON PAGE 32.

How many sea creatures?

Can you count how many of each sea creature there is and then write it in the box?

Sunken ship

Help Baby Shark find the sunken ship's treasure! Read the clues and cross out the squares until you're left with one square.

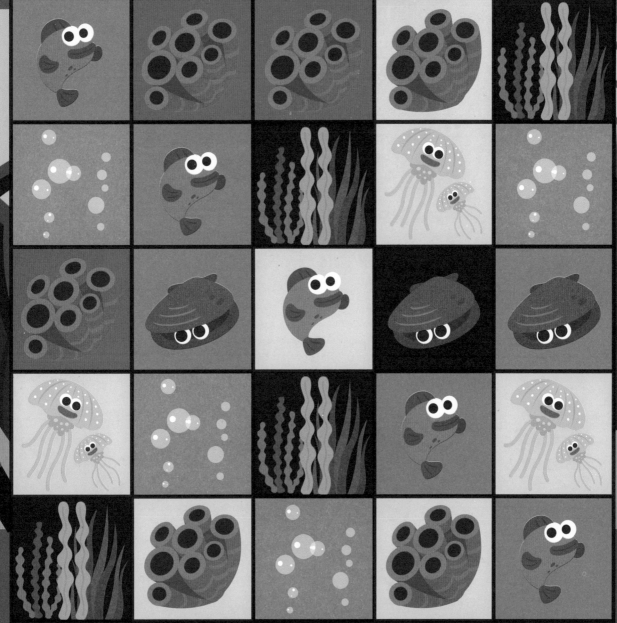

Treasure clues

1 The treasure isn't in a green square.

2 It's not in a square with bubbles.

3 It's not in a pink square.

4 You won't find the treasure in a square with William or a jellyfish.

5 It's not in a square with seaweed or coral.

Hooray for beach day

Grandma Shark has drawn a list of all the important things to take to the beach. Find each item on the list in the picture.

Which item on the list is missing?

Build with Baby Shark!

Read Baby Shark's top tips for building the ultimate sandcastle!

Ask an adult before you start to help you make this.

1 First of all you'll need some sand. Add some water to your sand to make it slightly damp.

2 Next you'll need something to put the sand in. Buckets are good but you can also ask an adult to help you find:
- Yoghurt pots
- Bowls
- Saucepans
- Plastic bottles cut in half

3 Come up with a design for your castle, you can draw out your castle first or just build it and see what happens! Both are super fun ways to create.

4 A spade is good to use but you can also use a spoon or just your hands!

5 Make sure you decorate your castle. You can use pebbles, shells, leaves, sticks and even flower petals.

Doodle some decorations on Baby Shark's sandcastle.

27

Find some treasure!

What has Baby Shark found?
Can you draw over the lines
and colour the balloons in?

Shark Family Orchestra

The Shark family love to play music together, draw their instruments in for them.

'doo-doo-doo-doo-doo!'

Daddy Shark

Fish Bus drops Daddy Shark and Baby Shark off at clue number two.
"We're blue and orange and have sixteen legs between us. Who could that mean, Baby Shark?" asks Daddy.

Vroom
Vroom

Clue 2

We're blue and orange and have sixteen legs between us.

Baby Shark points to the Octopus Sisters.
"I think they're right here," he says.

The Octopus Sisters hand clue number three to Daddy Shark and Baby Shark.

"Take a ride in me, I'm pink and I go deep!"

Clue 3

Take a ride in me, I'm pink and I go deep!

Baby Shark tugs on Daddy Shark's fin,

"I know this one," he points to Baby Seahorse.

Daddy Shark shakes his head, "I don't think

Baby Seahorse will take us deep in the ocean,

Baby Shark. We need to think again."

Just then a pink submarine pops up.
"Baby Shark, this is it!" says Daddy Shark.
They climb aboard and the
pink submarine gives
them the fourth clue.

The fourth clue just has a picture
of a giant sandcastle.
"I know where that is!" shouts Baby Shark
and he leads Daddy Shark back to
Grandma Shark and Grandpa Shark.

Clue 4

CONTINUED ON PAGE 48.

39

Spot the difference

Look at the sharks below and work out which one in each line up is different. Circle them with a pen.

1

2

3

4

5

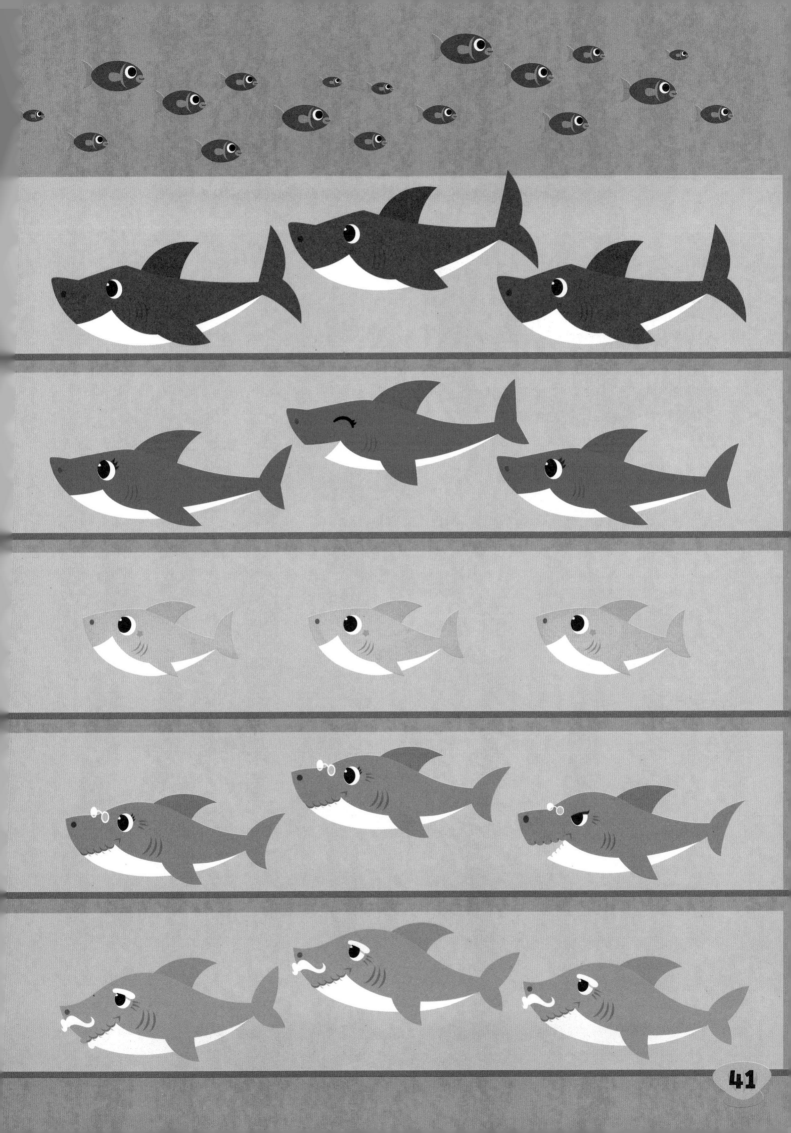

Find and colour

Instructions:
Make all the seahorses red.
Make all the shells yellow.
Make the turtles green.
Make the octopuses blue.

It's a busy day under the sea! Follow the instructions to find and colour the sea creatures.

Don't forget to colour in the Shark family!

42

As you colour sing the Baby Shark song!

43

Busy sea!

Colour in this sea scene. Make all the fish different bright colours!

Balloons for everyone

Draw each of Baby Shark's friends a balloon. What colour will you give them?

Daddy Shark

"You made it!" says Grandpa Shark.
"Here is the final clue." He hands a picture
of a shipwreck to Baby Shark.
Daddy Shark and Baby Shark
swim off to the shipwreck.

Clue 5

Next to the shipwreck
is a chest.
"Wow!" says Baby Shark.
"There really is treasure!"
Daddy Shark looks
at the chest.
It has a sign on it.
"To open me you
must sing!"

"Come on, then, Daddy Shark,"
says Baby Shark.
They sing a song together,
"Doo-doo-doo-doo-doo-doo!"
Everyone joins in.

"Doo-doo-doo-doo-doo-doo!"

'Doo-doo-doo-doo-doo-doo!'

"Look, Daddy Shark,"
says Baby Shark.
"The chest has opened!"

Daddy Shark and Baby Shark swim
back to Mummy Shark.

"Thanks for my treasure hunt," says Baby Shark.
"I couldn't have done it without you," says
Daddy Shark.

'Doo-doo-doo-doo-doo-doo!'

THE END!

Shadow sharks

Can you tell whose shadow belongs to who? Draw a line between each shark and their shadow.

1

2

3

4

5

a

b

c

d

e

Join in!

Would you like to join the Shark Family Orchestra and sing a song?

Draw yourself or stick a picture into the space and choose an instrument you'd like to play from below.

Picture time!

Baby Shark loves to draw, he's painting a great picture, can you colour it in for him?

Now you can draw your own picture and colour it in too!

Shark spiral

Circle every third letter in the shark spiral to complete the phrase below.

START

E · E · B · Q · N · S · K · W · N · H · A · O · H · J · B · D · A · U · I · Y · L · T · R · U · K · P · L

FINISH

_ _ _ _ _ _ _ _ _,
doo-doo-doo-doo-doo-doo!

Sharky jokes

The Shark family love to tell jokes. Which joke do you think is the funniest? Colour a star next to the one that makes you giggle the most.

What's scarier than a shark?

A HUNGRY SHARK!

What do you say to a shark telling a joke?

YOU'RE SO FINNY!

What do sharks fear the most?

THE DENTIST!

How do you make a milkshake?

GIVE IT A GOOD SCARE!

What happened to the shark that got famous?

IT BECAME A STARFISH!

Find the family

Baby Shark is here but where is his family? Trace the lines and draw them in for him. Now colour them all in!

Hide and seek

Baby Shark is playing hide and seek with William, but William keeps moving. See if you can find all of his hiding places.

Top tip! There are six places William has been hiding!

Hammerhead Shark's home!

Can you help Baby Shark guide Hammerhead Shark home?

3

1

2

HOME

Shark encounter!

Each of these close-up pictures belongs to one of the Sharks below. Can you work out which one for each picture?

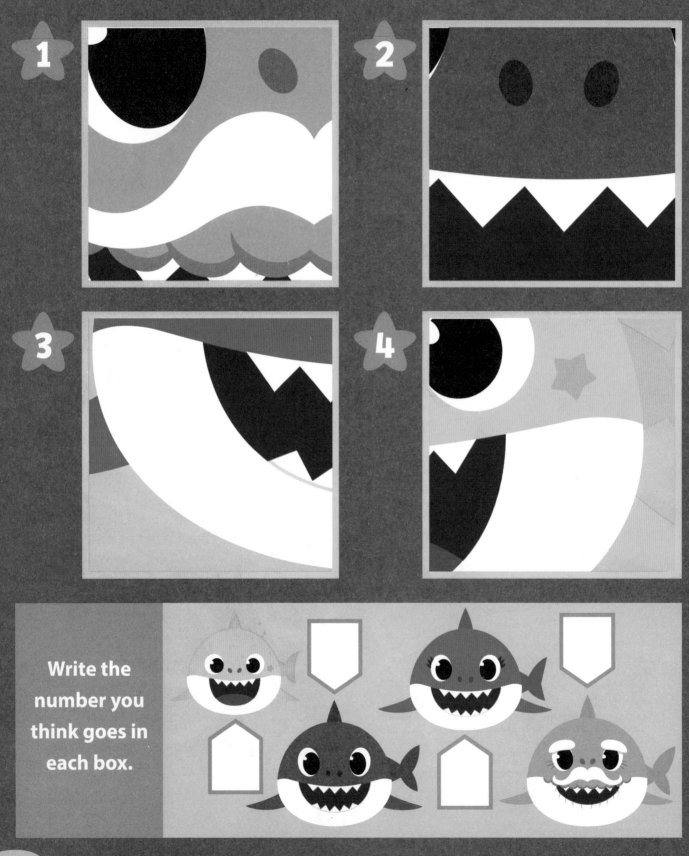

Write the number you think goes in each box.

Spot the difference

Can you work out what has changed between these two pictures? There are five differences to spot.

LOVE

LIVE

Family time

The Baby Shark family love to be together.
Colour them all in!

Grandma Shark and Grandpa Shark are such fun!

Find Baby Shark

Mummy Shark is looking for Baby Shark, can you help her through the maze to rescue him?

START

END

Let the starfish lead you to Baby Shark!

Odd one out

One of these pictures of Baby Shark is different to the rest, can you spot it?

71

Friends forever

Baby Shark loves to play with his friends.
What colour will you make all their balloons?

72

Singing time!

Baby Shark loves to sing, can you colour him in and sing along with him?

'doo-doo-doo-doo-doo-doo!'

Where's Baby Shark?

Everyone is looking for Baby Shark.
Can you find him?

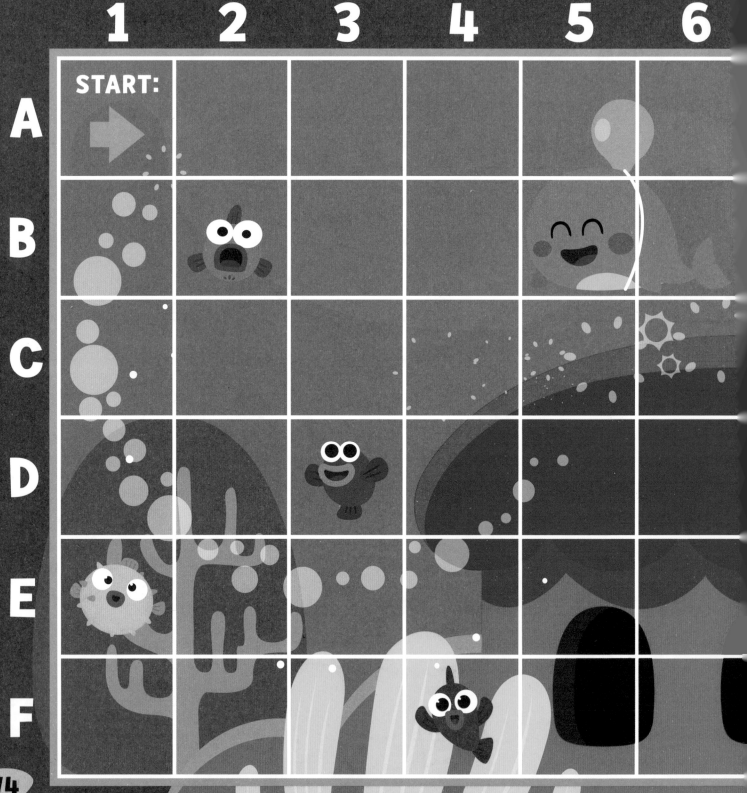

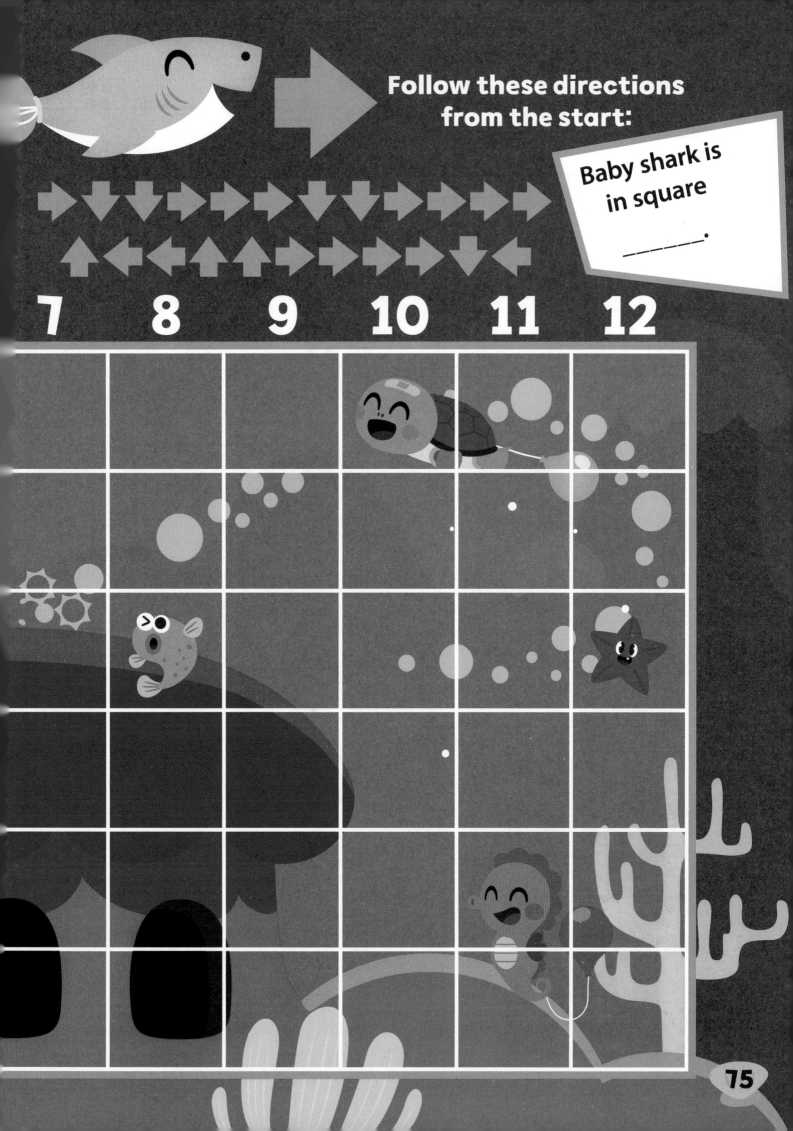

Follow these directions from the start:

Baby shark is in square

_____.

7   8   9   10   11   12

Answers

Pages 10–11

Colour quiz questions

1. What colour is Baby Shark?
2. What colour is Daddy Shark?
3. What colour is Mummy Shark?
4. What colour is Grandma Shark?
5. What colour is Grandpa Shark?
6. What colour is the jellyfish?
7. What colour is the starfish?
8. What colour is the turtle?

Page 24

Seahorses – 3   Octopus – 2
William – 6   Starfish – 6
Purple fish – 4   Whale – 1

Page 25

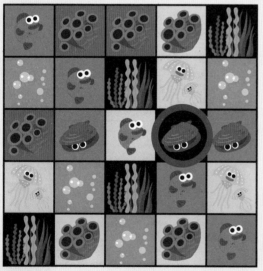

Page 26

Pages 40–41

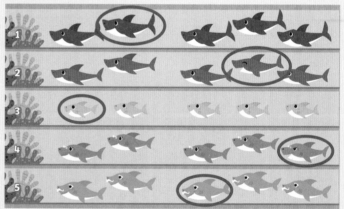

Page 56

1 – d   2 – c   3 – b
4 – e   5 – a

Page 60

BABY SHARK, doo-doo-doo-doo-doo-doo!

Page 64

Top tip!
There are six places William has been hiding!

Page 65

HOME

Page 66

Page 70

START
END

Page 71

Page 74–75

Baby shark is in square: C10

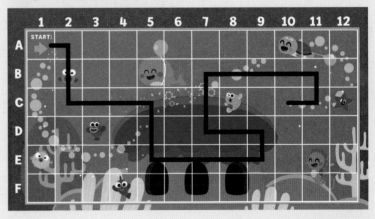

77